Edgar
Allan Poe's
The Raven
& Other Tales

Edgar Allan Poe's The Raven & Other Tales

& Other Tales

A Graphic Novel

ILLUSTRATED BY PETE KATZ

METRO BOOKS
New York

METRO BOOKS
New York

An Imprint of Sterling Publishing Co., Inc.
1166 Avenue of the Americas
New York, NY 10036

ISBN 978-1-4351-6152-8

For information about custom editions, special sales, and
premium and corporate purchases, please contact
Sterling Special Sales at 800-805-5489
or specialsales@sterlingpublishing.com.

Manufactured in China

2 4 6 8 10 9 7 5 3

www.sterlingpublishing.com

Contents

Introduction

As is the case with many other famous creatives, Edgar Allan Poe's greatness was only recognized after his death. For the majority of his career he was better known as a critic than an author in his own right. He did try to support himself with his writing alone, and was one of the first well-known American writers to try this—but he was unsuccessful. To support himself Poe worked at various publications from 1835 to 1846. Starting as assistant editor at the *Southern Literary Messenger*, he worked up to becoming owner of the *Broadway Journal* in 1845, which unfortunately went bust in 1846. During this time he wrote the short stories that appear in this book: "The Fall of the House of Usher" (1839), "The Masque of the Red Death" (1842), "The Black Cat" (1843), and "The System of Doctor Tarr and Professor Fether" (1845).

Poe's writing never made him rich, and his works always met with a lukewarm reaction. He had managed to make a name for himself with his reviews and articles but it wasn't till the release of *The Raven* in 1845 that he became a household name. Despite the huge popularity of the poem, he was only paid 9 dollars for its publication.

Much of Poe's writing is viewed as a master class in Gothic literature. This is partly because his works feature the core elements of Gothic fiction—horror, death, and romance—and often take place in the sort of eerie, mock-medieval buildings from which the movement takes its name. It is also because Poe's works provide the desired reaction from any decent Gothic piece: a pleasing fear or dread.

Poe believed that the true meaning of a piece of art must lie just below the surface. Works with obvious meanings, he once wrote, cease to be art. So, I hope I have approached his works with enough information to keep the narrative going but left enough unanswered questions for your imagination to resolve. As long as the reader is unsettled by the events, then Poe is happy.

Dramatis Personae

The Raven

THE MAN

THE RAVEN

The Fall of the House of Usher

**RODERICK
USHER**

MADELEINE

THE FRIEND

The Masque of the Red Death

PROSPERO

THE RED DEATH

The Black Cat

THE BLACK CAT

THE MAN

THE WIFE

The System of Doctor Tarr and Professor Fether

MARCEL

MONSIEUR
MAILLARD

CLAUDE

The Raven

ONCE UPON A MIDNIGHT DREARY,
WHILE I PONDERED, WEAK AND WEARY,
OVER MANY A QUAINT AND CURIOUS
VOLUME OF FORGOTTEN LORE--

Tap   Tap

WHILE I NODDED, NEARLY NAPPING,
SUDDENLY THERE CAME A TAPPING,
AS OF SOME ONE GENTLY RAPPING,
RAPPING AT MY CHAMBER DOOR.

'TIS SOME VISITOR TAPPING AT MY
CHAMBER DOOR--
ONLY THIS, AND NOTHING MORE.

AH, DISTINCTLY I REMEMBER
IT WAS IN THE BLEAK DECEMBER,
AND EACH SEPARATE DYING EMBER
WROUGHT ITS GHOST UPON THE FLOOR.

EAGERLY I WISHED THE MORROW
--VAINLY I HAD SOUGHT TO BORROW
FROM MY BOOKS SURCEASE OF SORROW
--SORROW FOR THE LOST LENORE.

FOR THE RARE AND RADIANT MAIDEN
WHOM THE ANGELS NAME LENORE--
NAMELESS HERE FOR EVERMORE.

AND THE SILKEN SAD UNCERTAIN RUSTLING
OF EACH PURPLE CURTAIN
THRILLED ME--FILLED ME WITH FANTASTIC
TERRORS NEVER FELT BEFORE;

SO THAT NOW, TO STILL THE BEATING
OF MY HEART, I STOOD REPEATING,

'TIS SOME VISITOR ENTREATING
ENTRANCE AT MY CHAMBER DOOR.
SOME LATE VISITOR ENTREATING
ENTRANCE AT MY CHAMBER DOOR.
THIS IT IS AND NOTHING MORE.

PRESENTLY MY SOUL GREW STRONGER;
HESITATING THEN NO LONGER,

SIR, OR MADAM, TRULY YOUR
FORGIVENESS I IMPLORE.
BUT THE FACT IS I WAS NAPPING,
AND SO GENTLY YOU CAME TAPPING
AT MY CHAMBER DOOR,
THAT I SCARCE WAS SURE
I HEARD YOU.

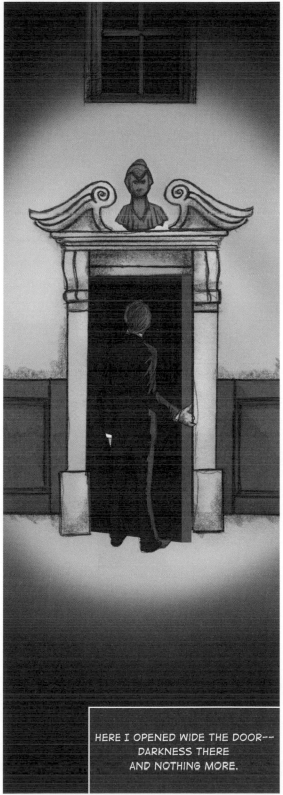

HERE I OPENED WIDE THE DOOR--
DARKNESS THERE
AND NOTHING MORE.

DEEP INTO THAT DARKNESS PEERING,
LONG I STOOD THERE WONDERING, FEARING,
DOUBTING, DREAMING
DREAMS NO MORTALS EVER DARED TO
DREAM BEFORE.

BUT THE SILENCE WAS UNBROKEN,
AND THE STILLNESS GAVE NO TOKEN,
AND THE ONLY WORD THERE SPOKEN
WAS THE WHISPERED WORD,

LENORE?

OPEN HERE
I FLUNG THE SHUTTER,
WHEN, WITH MANY
A FLIRT AND FLUTTER...

...IN THERE STEPPED
A STATELY RAVEN OF THE
SAINTLY DAYS OF YORE.

NOT THE LEAST OBEISANCE
MADE HE; NOT A MINUTE
STOPPED
OR STAYED HE,

BUT, WITH MIEN OF LORD OR
LADY, PERCHED ABOVE MY
CHAMBER DOOR.

HE PERCHED UPON A BUST
OF PALLAS JUST ABOVE MY
CHAMBER DOOR--

PERCHED, AND SAT,
AND NOTHING MORE.

THEN THIS EBONY BIRD
BEGUILING MY SAD FANCY
INTO SMILING,
BY THE GRAVE AND
STERN DECORUM
OF THE COUNTENANCE
IT WORE.

THOUGH THY
CREST BE SHORN
AND SHAVEN,
THOU ART SURE
NO CRAVEN,
GHASTLY GRIM AND
ANCIENT RAVEN
WANDERING FROM
THE NIGHTLY SHORE.

TELL ME WHAT THY
LORDLY NAME IS
ON THE NIGHT'S
PLUTONIAN SHORE!

NEVERMORE

MUCH I MARVELED THIS UNGAINLY FOWL
TO HEAR DISCOURSE SO PLAINLY,
THOUGH ITS ANSWER LITTLE MEANING--
LITTLE RELEVANCY BORE.

BUT THE RAVEN, SITTING LONELY
ON THE PLACID BUST, SPOKE ONLY
THAT ONE WORD, AS IF ITS SOUL IN THAT ONE WORD
HE DID OUTPOUR.
NOTHING FURTHER THEN HE UTTERED; NOT A
FEATHER THEN HE FLUTTERED.

BUT THE RAVEN STILL BEGUILING
ALL MY SADNESS INTO SMILING,
STRAIGHT I WHEELED A CUSHIONED SEAT
IN FRONT OF BIRD AND BUST AND DOOR.

THEN UPON THE VELVET SINKING,
I BETOOK MYSELF TO LINKING
FANCY UNTO FANCY,
THINKING WHAT THIS OMINOUS BIRD OF YORE--
WHAT THIS GRIM, UNGAINLY, GHASTLY, GAUNT,
AND OMINOUS BIRD OF YORE
MEANT IN CROAKING "NEVERMORE."

THIS I SAT ENGAGED IN GUESSING, BUT NO SYLLABLE EXPRESSING

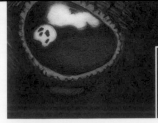

TO THE FOWL WHOSE FIERY EYES NOW BURNED INTO MY BOSOM'S CORE.

THIS AND MORE I SAT DIVINING, WITH MY HEAD AT EASE RECLINING ON THE CUSHION'S VELVET LINING THAT THE LAMPLIGHT GLOATED O'ER.

SHE SHALL PRESS, AH, NEVERMORE!

THEN METHOUGHT THE AIR GREW DENSER, PERFUMED FROM AN UNSEEN CENSER

SWUNG BY SERAPHIM WHOSE FOOT-FALLS TINKLED ON THE TUFTED FLOOR.

WRETCH!

THY GOD HATH LENT THEE-- BY THESE ANGELS HE HATH SENT THEE!

RESPITE--RESPITE AND NEPENTHE, FROM THY MEMORIES OF LENORE! QUAFF, OH QUAFF THIS KIND NEPENTHE, AND FORGET THIS LOST LENORE!

NEVERMORE

AND THE RAVEN, NEVER FLITTING, STILL IS SITTING, STILL IS SITTING
ON THE PALLID BUST OF PALLAS JUST ABOVE MY CHAMBER DOOR.
AND HIS EYES HAVE ALL THE SEEMING OF A DEMON'S THAT IS DREAMING,
AND THE LAMPLIGHT O'ER HIM STREAMING THROWS HIS SHADOW ON THE FLOOR.
AND MY SOUL FROM OUT THAT SHADOW THAT LIES FLOATING ON THE FLOOR
SHALL BE LIFTED...NEVERMORE!

The Fall of
The House of Usher

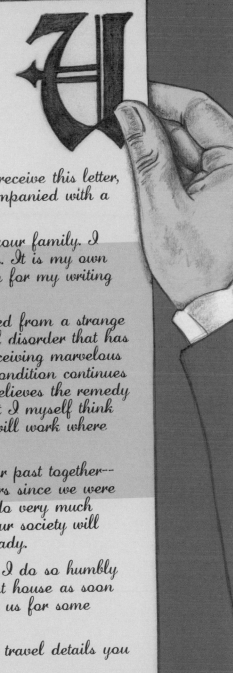

My dear friend,

You will no doubt be surprised to receive this letter, but I do hope the surprise is accompanied with a degree of pleasure.

My warmest regards to you and your family. I hope they are in the best of health. It is my own health which is the singular reason for my writing to you.

For some time now I have suffered from a strange and acute bodily illness—a mental disorder that has continued to oppress me. I am receiving marvelous care from our physician, but my condition continues to confound him. He, of course, believes the remedy will come in a vial or tincture, but I myself think some friendly and warm society will work where medicine has not.

I have such fond memories of our past together—and though it has been many years since we were boon companions of boyhood, I do very much believe that the cheerfulness of your society will offer some alleviation of my malady.

And so, my best and only friend, I do so humbly request that you travel to our great house as soon as you are able and sojourn with us for some weeks.

I will write later in this letter the travel details you will need...

GOOD AFTERNOON. WOULD YOU MIND IF I RODE ALONGSIDE YOU A WHILE? THE LANDSCAPE ROUND HERE IS UNCOMMONLY DREARY AND I WOULD WELCOME SOME COMPANY FOR A CHANGE.

BY ALL MEANS.

ARE YOU ON YOUR WAY TO TOWN?

NO, I'M VISITING A FRIEND WHOSE FAMILY ESTATE I'M ASSURED IS NOT FAR FROM HERE.

DO YOU MEAN THE USHERS?

I DO INDEED. ARE YOU ACQUAINTED WITH THEM?

ONLY BY REPUTATION I'M AFRAID. STRANGE FAMILY. STRANGE FAMILY AT BEST.

PECULIAR TEMPERAMENT THAT LENDS ITSELF TO THE ARTISTIC AND MUSICAL PRACTICES. I HEAR MANY EXALTED WORKS CAME OUT OF THAT HOUSE, AS WELL AS MANY DEEDS OF MUNIFICENT YET UNOBTRUSIVE CHARITY.

WHAT IS THIS SICKENING OF HEART I FEEL? WHAT IS IT THAT UNNERVES ME SO? WHAT IS THIS DULL, SLUGGISH ATMOSPHERE THAT SURROUNDS THE HOUSE? I MUST BE IMAGINING IT. I AM TIRED FROM THE RIDE AFTER ALL.

MAY I
ASK...

MY DEAR FRIEND, IT IS A SHEER DELIGHT TO SEE YOU AGAIN.

IT IS VERY GOOD TO SEE YOU AGAIN TOO, USHER.

MY GOD. NO MAN HAS SURELY EVER BEEN SO ALTERED IN SO FEW YEARS.

USHER. MY GOOD FELLOW. WHAT HAS HAPPENED TO YOU?

AM I THAT MUCH CHANGED? YES, I SUPPOSE I MUST BE. YOU FIND ME AT MY WORST, MY FRIEND. THE MALADY I SUFFER UNDER IS, I BELIEVE, A CONSTITUTIONAL AND FAMILY EVIL.

IT DISPLAYS ITSELF IN A HOST OF UNNATURAL SENSATIONS. I SUFFER MUCH FROM A MORBID ACUTENESS OF THE SENSES: THE MOST INSIPID FOOD IS ALONE ENDURABLE...

I CAN WEAR ONLY GARMENTS OF CERTAIN TEXTURE; THE ODOR OF ALL FLOWERS IS OPPRESSIVE; MY EYES ARE TORTURED BY EVEN A FAINT LIGHT, AND ONLY CERTAIN SOUNDS DO NOT INSPIRE ME WITH HORROR.

IT WILL UNDOUBTEDLY SOON PASS.

LET US HOPE SO.

BUT I AM SLAVE TO TERROR, YOU SEE. I SHALL PERISH, I MUST PERISH IN THIS DEPLORABLE FOLLY.

THUS, THUS, AND NOT OTHERWISE, SHALL I BE LOST.

I DREAD THE EVENTS OF THE FUTURE, NOT IN THEMSELVES, BUT IN THEIR RESULTS. I SHUDDER AT THE THOUGHT OF ANY, EVEN THE MOST TRIVIAL, INCIDENT, WHICH MAY OPERATE UPON THIS INTOLERABLE AGITATION OF SOUL.

I HAVE, INDEED, NO ABHORRENCE OF DANGER, EXCEPT IN ITS ABSOLUTE EFFECT...IN TERROR.

IN THIS PITIABLE CONDITION...I FEEL THAT SOONER OR LATER I MUST ABANDON LIFE AND REASON, IN SOME STRUGGLE WITH THE GRIM PHANTASM...

...FEAR.

AH, YOUR REFRESHMENT. GOOD. PLEASE, MY FRIEND. EAT YOUR FILL.

I AM TIRED, AS I AM SURE YOU ARE. SO I WILL SAY GOOD NIGHT. AMBROSE HERE WILL SHOW YOU TO YOUR QUARTERS WHEN YOU ARE READY. GOOD NIGHT.

A FEW DAYS LATER...

I SAW A GENTLEMAN LEAVE EARLIER.

OH YES, MR. SHARP. MY ATTORNEY. HE COMES TWICE WEEKLY TO KEEP ME ABREAST OF ALL MY BUSINESS DEALINGS.

VERY GOOD OF HIM TO RIDE ALL THE WAY OUT HERE SO OFTEN WHILE YOU ARE ILL.

SHARP HAS ALWAYS COME HERE. I NEVER GO INTO TOWN. I NEVER GO ANYWHERE.

ANYWHERE?

NO, OF COURSE NOT. I CAN'T GO ANYWHERE.

I AM LINKED FOREVER TO THIS DWELLING. ⋛SIGH⋜ I HAVE NO DOUBT IT CONTRIBUTES TO MY CONDITION, BUT I AM EQUALLY CERTAIN IF I ATTEMPTED TO LEAVE I WOULD SURELY PERISH. IT IS THE USHER CURSE. WE CANNOT ESCAPE IT.

WE?

MYSELF AND MY SISTER, MADELINE. MY LAST AND ONLY RELATIVE ON EARTH. MY SOLE COMPANION FOR THESE LONG, LONELY YEARS IS GRAVELY ILL. SO ILL, IN FACT, THAT I DO BELIEVE HER NOT LONG FOR THIS WORLD. AND HER DECEASE WILL LEAVE ME THE LAST OF THE ANCIENT RACE OF THE USHERS.

I HAD NO IDEA YOU EVEN HAD...

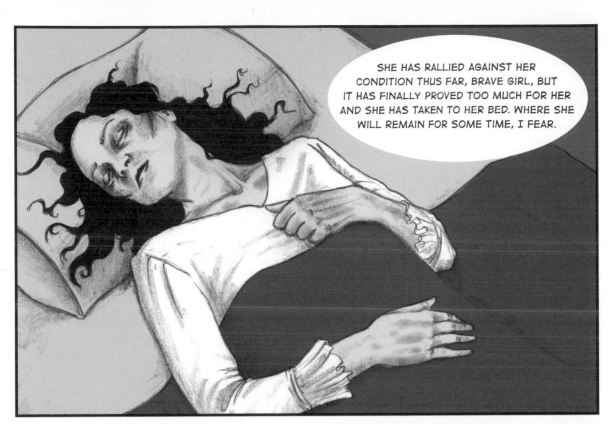

SOME DAYS LATER, RODERICK MADE AN ANNOUNCEMENT...

MY SISTER IS DEAD.

OH, RODERICK. MY POOR FELLOW, I'M SO SORRY. IF THERE IS ANYTHING I CAN DO?

ACTUALLY, THERE IS SOMETHING. I DO NOT TRUST THE SERVANTS TO IT. WOULD YOU HELP ME CARRY MY SISTER TO THE VAULTS? HER FUNERAL WILL BE IN A FORTNIGHT BUT IN THE MEANTIME, I REFUSE TO HAND HER OVER TO THOSE MEDICAL VULTURES.

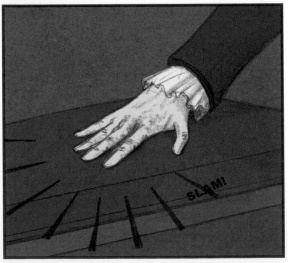

THE NEXT DAY...

THREE DAYS LATER...

SEVEN DAYS LATER...

55

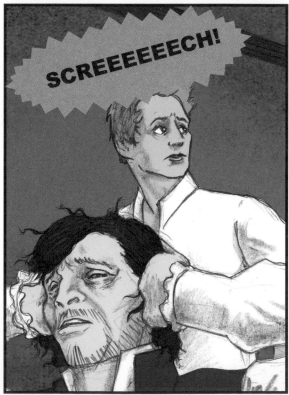

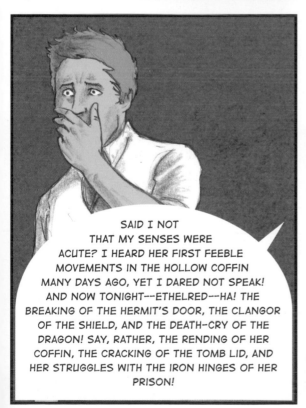

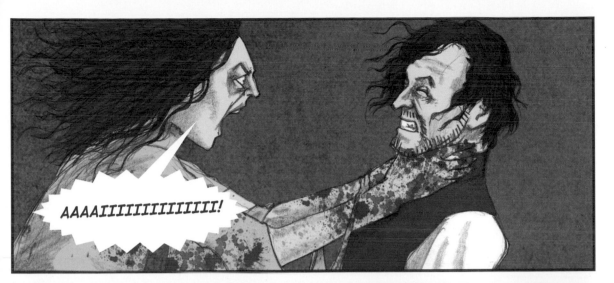

AAAAIIIIIIIIIIII!

HELP! HELP! AMBROSE! ANYONE!

The Masque
of the Red Death

THE "RED DEATH" HAD LONG DEVASTATED THE COUNTRY.
NO PESTILENCE HAD EVER BEEN SO FATAL, OR SO HIDEOUS. BLOOD WAS ITS
AVATAR AND ITS SEAL---THE REDNESS AND THE HORROR OF BLOOD.

THERE WERE SHARP PAINS, AND SUDDEN DIZZINESS, AND THEN PROFUSE BLEEDING AT THE PORES, WITH DISSOLUTION.

THE SCARLET STAINS UPON THE BODY AND ESPECIALLY UPON THE FACE OF THE VICTIM SHUT HIM OUT FROM THE AID AND FROM THE SYMPATHY OF HIS FELLOW MEN.

BUT THE PRINCE PROSPERO WAS HAPPY AND DAUNTLESS AND SAGACIOUS. WHEN HIS DOMINIONS WERE HALF DEPOPULATED, HE SUMMONED TO HIS PRESENCE HALE AND LIGHT-HEARTED FRIENDS FROM AMONG THE NOBLES OF HIS COURT, AND WITH THESE RETIRED TO DEEP SECLUSION.

WELCOME, FRIENDS, WELCOME! WITHOUT THESE WALLS THE RED DEATH REIGNS BUT I PROMISE YOU SECURITY WITHIN. YOU WILL FIND EVERYTHING HAS BEEN PROVIDED FOR. DO NOT GRIEVE, DO NOT THINK. MAKE MERRY. LET THE EXTERNAL WORLD TAKE CARE OF ITSELF.

THE GATES WERE SEALED.

AND THE GUARDS HAD THEIR ORDERS.

KILL ANYTHING THAT TRIES TO GET IN. OR OUT.

AND THE GATES HELD. AND THE GUARDS WATCHED. AND NOTHING GAINED ENTRY TO PROSPERO'S KEEP.

BUT THIS DID NOT DAUNT THE RED DEATH.

ONCE HE TRAVELED WITH A FISH TO SWIM UP THE STREAM THAT ORIGINATED AT THE FORTRESS WELL.

BUT PROSPERO HAD BUILT A GATE.

ONCE HE TRAVELED WITH A BIRD TO FLY OVER THE HIGH WALLS.

BUT THE GUARDS HAD THEIR ORDERS.

AT THE END OF EVERY MONTH, PROSPERO WOULD CLIMB THE BATTLEMENTS TO GLOAT...

ANOTHER MONTH SAFE, FIEND! ANOTHER MONTH THAT THE GREAT STAG HAS OUTWITTED YOU!

IT WAS TOWARD THE CLOSE OF THE SIXTH MONTH OF HIS SECLUSION, AND WHILE THE PESTILENCE RAGED MOST FURIOUSLY ABROAD, THAT PRINCE PROSPERO ENTERTAINED HIS FRIENDS AT A MASKED BALL OF THE MOST UNUSUAL MAGNIFICENCE.

AH, LADY AGNES! HOW MARVELOUS TO SEE YOU AT LAST AFTER ALL THESE WEEKS! I WAS BEGINNING TO BELIEVE YOU HAD EXPIRED IN YOUR ROOM.

I'M SORRY, MY LORD, FOR MY POOR ATTENDANCE, BUT I FIND THE CELEBRATIONS SOMEWHAT... EXCESSIVE.

EXCESSIVE, EH? TELL ME, MY LADY, HAVE WE NOT FED YOU THESE LAST SIX MONTHS? AND KEPT YOU SAFE FROM THE HORRORS OUTSIDE?

YES, MY LORD.

THEN I WOULD SAY THAT IF ANYTHING IS EXCESSIVE HERE, IT IS YOUR LACK OF GRATITUDE. YOUR DESIRE TO SHUN ALL OF US, YOUR GOOD FRIENDS! IS THIS NOT EXCESSIVELY DISRESPECTFUL?

I DO BELIEVE YOU, AGNES. AND TO PROVE THERE IS NO BAD FEELING BETWEEN US I WILL PERSONALLY TAKE YOU ON A TOUR OF THE CHAMBERS. I BELIEVE YOU HAVE NEVER ENTERED THEM.

I MEANT NO DISRESPECT, MY LORD. PLEASE BELIEVE ME.

YOU DO ME TOO MUCH HONOR, MY LORD.

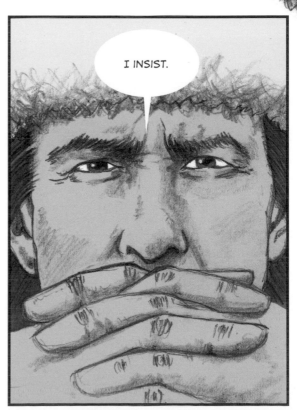

I INSIST.

THE FINAL ROOM. WHERE ONLY ONE INHABITANT RESIDES.

FOUL CLOCK. IF ONLY I COULD HAVE YOU PUT TO THE BLADE AS EASILY.

YOU ARE THE ONLY REMINDER OF THE PASSING OF TIME LEFT WITHIN MY HOUSE. AND YOUR CHIME SICKENS ALL WHO HEAR IT.

I WOULD HAVE HAD YOU BURNED LIKE ALL THE OTHER CLOCKS IF I DIDN'T BELIEVE YOU CURSED. WRETCHED THING.

AS IF IN ANSWER...

BONG!

BONG!

BONG!

GOOD EVENING.

IT HAS BEEN SOME TIME SINCE I SAW FRUIT OF SUCH QUALITY. WHERE DID YOU COME BY IT, CHILD?

HA HA HA HA HA HA HA!

WHY DO YOU THINK THAT?

WELL, YOU HAVE A LOVELY SOFT VOICE AND THE OTHER DAY I SAW YOU WALKIN' ON WATER. SO WHO ELSE COULD YA BE?

IT IS TRUE I HAVE HELD OTHER NAMES BEFORE, BUT NEVER THAT ONE. TELL ME, CLEVER GIRL, WILL YOU SHOW ME YOUR SECRET WAY INTO THE FORTRESS?

I WILL.

COZ YOU'RE THE ONLY PERSON WHO HASN'T TRIED TO EAT MY FOOD, HURT ME, OR KILL ME IN WEEKS.

I THANK YOU AGAIN, CHILD. YOU HAVE BEEN BOTH KIND AND A JOY. I WILL NOT FORGET THAT.

WHO DARES?
WHO DARES INSULT US BY DRESSING AS THE RED DEATH ITSELF? SEIZE HIM AND UNMASK HIM--SO THAT WE KNOW WHO IT IS WE HANG FROM THE BATTLEMENTS!

DAMN COWARDS! I SHALL DO IT MYSELF!

WHO ARE YOU?

YOU KNOW VERY WELL WHO I AM, PROSPERO.

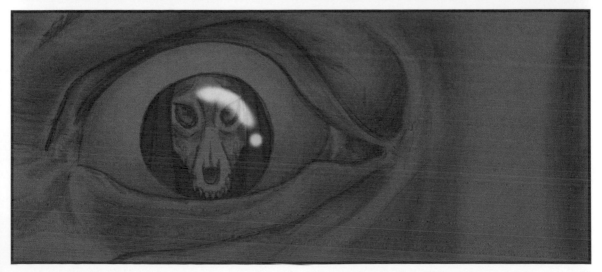

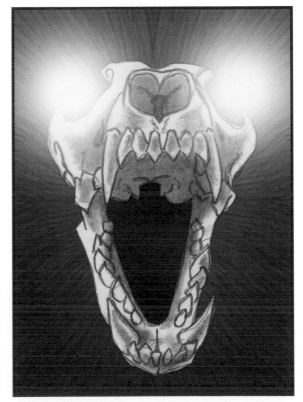

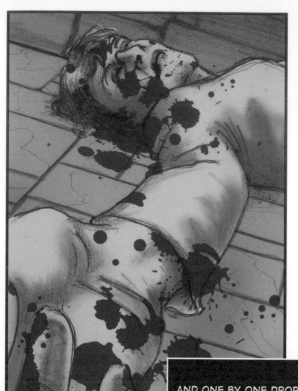

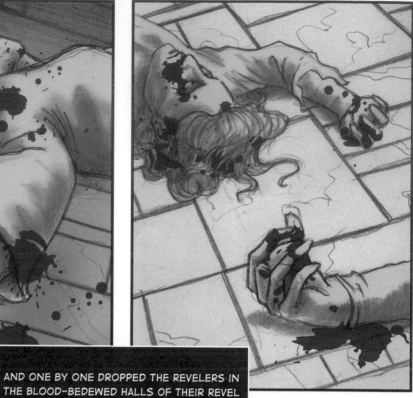

AND ONE BY ONE DROPPED THE REVELERS IN THE BLOOD-BEDEWED HALLS OF THEIR REVEL AND DIED EACH IN THE DESPAIRING POSTURE OF HIS FALL.

AND THE LIFE OF THE EBONY CLOCK WENT OUT
WITH THAT OF THE LAST OF THE MERRY. AND
DARKNESS AND DECAY AND THE RED DEATH
HELD ILLIMITABLE DOMINION OVER ALL.

The Black Cat

NEWGATE PRISON.

DO YOU LIKE ANIMALS, FATHER? DO YOU OWN ANY PETS?

ER. I AM FOND OF DOGS, AS IT HAPPENS. I HAVE A LITTLE JACK RUSSELL. PIP.

AH, YES. FINE CREATURES, DOGS. VERY UNCOMPLICATED; SO FORGIVING AND LOYAL. THERE IS SOMETHING PURE IN THE UNSELFISH LOVE OF A BRUTE THAT PUTS TO SHAME THE PALTRY FRIENDSHIPS OF HUMANS. DO YOU NOT THINK SO, FATHER?

YOU TALK AS IF YOU PREFER ANIMALS TO YOUR FELLOW MAN.

INDEED I DID FATHER. FOR ALMOST MY ENTIRE LIFE.

SINCE CHILDHOOD I WAS INDULGED AND HAVE HAD MANY PETS. WHEN I MARRIED AT A FAIRLY YOUNG AGE IT WAS TO A WOMAN WHOSE DISPOSITION TO ANIMALS WAS COMMON TO MY OWN.

AND FOR SOME YEARS WE LIVED IN HAPPINESS WITH OUR LITTLE MENAGERIE. CAROLINE HAD HER FAVORITES, BUT MINE WAS OUR CAT.

GOOD MORNING, CAROLINE.

PLUTO'S BEEN FED AND WATERED.

I INHERITED A FAIR AMOUNT OF MONEY AND WAS A PARTNER IN A NUMBER OF SMALL FIRMS. NOT ALL OF WHICH WERE PERFORMING SATISFACTORILY.

SALES ARE STILL DOWN, JACKSON! YOU ASSURED ME THAT GUNPOWDER WOULD BE A SECURE INVESTMENT. "THERE'LL ALWAYS BE WARS, SO THERE'LL ALWAYS BE GUNS." THAT'S WHAT YOU SAID! BUT THE ONLY PEOPLE BUYING THE DAMN STUFF ARE MINING COMPANIES!

I'M SORRY, SEBRIGHT. BUT SINCE DUPONT WON THE GOVERNMENT CONTRACT THEY'VE MANAGED TO SECURE MOST OF THE MARKET.

I DON'T WANT TO HEAR IT. I'M TELLING YOU, JACKSON, IF THAT DAMN FACTORY LOSES ME ANY MORE MONEY, THEN I'M GOING TO TAKE A MATCH TO THE PLACE. WHILE YOU'RE STILL IN IT!

I FEAR I WAS NOT BUILT FOR BUSINESS. THE VARIOUS INVESTMENTS I HAD MADE WERE NAIVE AND IMPRUDENT. AND THE SITUATION, WHILE NOT DESPERATE, WAS FAR FROM GOOD. BUT CAROLINE WAS SO SWEET AND UNSPOILED AT THAT TIME THAT I WANTED TO SPARE HER ANY WORRY.

SO BEFORE RETURNING HOME, I GOT INTO THE HABIT OF VISITING A GIN PALACE FOR A BRIEF SPELL. A QUICK DRINK HELPED CALM ME DOWN AND ALLEVIATE SOME OF THE DAY'S STRESS SO I COULD ARRIVE HOME MY USUAL SELF.

BUT AS THE WEEKS MOVED ON, THE FINANCIAL SITUATION GREW WORSE AND MY INTERMISSIONS AT THE GIN PALACE GREW LONGER AND LONGER. AND HOME, A PLACE I ONCE LOVED AND PROTECTED, BECAME IN MY HEAD, NO DOUBT OUT OF GUILT, A PLACE WHERE I WAS TO BE JUDGED AND INTERROGATED.

HOW WAS WORK TODAY, RICHARD?

AM I TO BE GRANTED NO PEACE?? I MUST WORK ALL DAY ANSWERING QUESTIONS ONLY TO COME HOME AND DO THE SAME HERE?

I AM ONLY WORRIED, RICHARD! I'M NOT AN IMBECILE! YOU TELL ME NOTHING, BUT YOU COME HOME FROM WORK MORE AND MORE UPSET EVERY DAY. ALMOST ALWAYS SMELLING OF BOOZE. YOU'RE EVEN HALF-DRUNK NOW! WHAT ON EARTH IS THE MATTER? SOMETHING IS WRONG!

EVERYTHING IS FINE! SO I LIKE A SMALL DRINK AFTER WORK! WHAT HARM IN THAT? I'LL TELL YOU WHAT, SINCE YOU ARE SUDDENLY SUCH AN ACCOMPLISHED BUSINESSWOMAN, FROM NEXT WEEK I SHALL START BRINGING HOME THE MONTHLY REPORTS SO THAT YOU CAN CAST YOUR PROFESSIONAL EYE OVER THEM! HERE! HAVE MY FINANCIAL TIMES, TOO!

I SHUDDER AT THE ATROCITY, FATHER. I BURN WITH SHAME. IN THE MORNING LIGHT OF SOBRIETY AND REALIZATION, I WAS FILLED WITH HORROR AND REMORSE.

AS FOR PLUTO, HE SLOWLY RECOVERED. HE SEEMED NO LONGER IN ANY PHYSICAL PAIN BUT, AS TO BE EXPECTED, HE COWERED AND EVEN FLED IN TERROR AT MY APPROACH. I WAS GRIEVED AT FIRST TO SEE HOW I HAD TURNED HIS LOVE OF ME TO FEAR.

BUT THIS FEELING SOON GAVE WAY TO IRRITATION AND IN TURN TO HATE. THE CONTINUAL COWERING PRESENCE OF THE POOR WRETCH WAS A CONSTANT REBUKE AND SEEMED TO BE THE ONLY THING THAT STILL TOUCHED ME WITH SHAME.

BUT MY GUILT WAS FEEBLE AND FLEETING, AND WITH THE HELP OF MY FAITHFUL FRIEND, GIN, I SOON DROWNED ALL MEMORY OF THE DEED. BUT THAT ONE VILE ACT HAD OPENED A DOOR IN ME. A DOOR INTO THE DARKEST PLACE OF MY BEING. A PLACE WHERE EVIL RESIDES AND HAD NOW BEEN RELEASED.

FROM THEN ON, I FOUND MYSELF DOING THINGS I KNEW TO BE WRONG, BUT I DID THEM ANYWAY FOR THAT PRECISE REASON. I TOOK PLEASURE IN THE KNOWLEDGE AND THE ACT.

SO, ONE MORNING, I RID MYSELF OF SHAME.

BUT THAT NIGHT...

MASTERS! MASTERS!

FIRE! THE HOUSE IS AFIRE!

OH, RICHARD.
WE ARE RUINED.

THE POOR
ANIMALS.

PLUTO'S BODY WAS GONE.

COULD IT HAVE BEEN THE WORK OF SOME ANIMAL LOVER?

I HASTILY LEFT THE SCENE AND TRIED TO PUT IT ALL FROM MY MIND.

I IMMEDIATELY SET ABOUT SELLING OFF MOST OF THE COMPANIES I HAD INVESTED IN. I MANAGED TO RAISE ENOUGH TO SET MYSELF AND CAROLINE UP IN A SOMEWHAT HUMBLER DWELLING. BUT MY HABITS REMAINED WICKED AND DISSOLUTE.

WHAT *IS* THAT?

WELL, WELL! AREN'T YOU A FINE, FRIENDLY FELLOW?

MISTER VINCENT! I DIDN'T KNOW YOU HAD A CAT.

PURRRRRR.

THE NEXT MORNING...

OH RICHARD, WHEREVER DID YOU FIND HIM?

HE LOOKS JUST LIKE POOR PLUTO!

APART FROM THE LITTLE WHITE MARK ON HIS NECK. HE EVEN HAS AN EYE MISSING TOO, THE POOR THING.

I HAD NOT NOTICED ITS MISSING EYE THE NIGHT BEFORE.

ANY WARMTH I HAD FELT FOR THE CAT INSTANTLY VANISHED. I FELT ONLY LOATHING AND DISGUST. CAROLINE WAS INSTANTLY ATTACHED TO THE THING, SO I DIDN'T WANT TO THROW HIM OUT. BUT I AVOIDED CONTACT WITH HIM AS MUCH AS POSSIBLE.

WHICH PROVED DIFFICULT AS MY AVERSION TO THE CAT SEEMED TO ONLY INCREASE ITS PARTIALITY FOR ME. AND OVER THE NEXT FEW WEEKS IT SEEMED DETERMINED TO BE MY SHADOW.

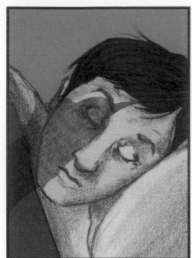

BUT SHE WAS RIGHT. I HAD BECOME SCARED OF THE CAT. I SCARCE KNOW WHEN THE FEELING AROSE, BUT I AM ALMOST ASHAMED TO ADMIT THAT THE ANIMAL'S PRESENCE FILLED ME WITH TERROR, HORROR, AND ABSOLUTE DREAD.

NO SMALL PART OF THIS DREAD WAS DUE TO A CERTAIN WHITE MARK ON THE CAT'S PERSON.

LOOK, RICHARD. HIS LITTLE WHITE MARK HAS GROWN ALL THE WAY ROUND. ISN'T IT ADORABLE? HE HAS HIS OWN LITTLE COLLAR!

OR A NOOSE!

AS IF THE BEAST KNEW I WAS SUCCUMBING TO MOUNTING FEAR, HE PUSHED HOME HIS ADVANTAGE AND GRANTED ME NEITHER ESCAPE NOR REST.

DURING THE DAY THE
CREATURE LEFT ME NO
MOMENT ALONE.

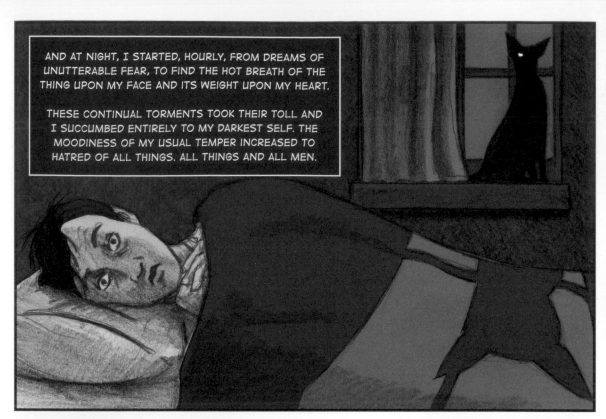

HURRY UP WITH THAT WOOD.

THE FIRE WILL... *AAAA!*

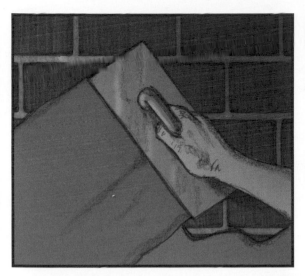

I THEN WENT LOOKING FOR THE SOURCE OF SO MUCH WRETCHEDNESS. THE ONLY WITNESS TO THE CRIME.

I WAS FILLED WITH A NEW, SAVAGE RESOLVE, AND IF I HAD FOUND THE CREATURE, HE WOULD HAVE MET THE SAME FATE AS MY WIFE.

AT LONG LAST. THE MONSTER HAS FLED. YOUR TURN TO FEEL TERROR, YOU WRETCH. DO NOT RETURN!

FOR THE NEXT FEW DAYS, I SLEPT SOUNDLY AND TRANQUILLY FOR THE FIRST TIME IN MONTHS, TROUBLED LITTLE BY GUILT OR FEAR OF DISCOVERY. ENQUIRES WERE MADE, A SEARCH WAS INSTITUTED---BUT OF COURSE NOTHING WAS DISCOVERED. I LOOKED UPON MY FUTURE FELICITY AS SECURED.

BUT ON THE FOURTH DAY AFTER THE MURDER, A PARTY OF POLICE ARRIVED UNEXPECTEDLY TO MAKE ANOTHER SEARCH OF THE PROPERTY.

IF YOU WOULDN'T MIND ACCOMPANYING US WHILE WE SEARCH, PLEASE SIR. WE'LL START AT THE TOP OF THE HOUSE.

NOTHING.

ARE YOU ALRIGHT, SIR? YOU SEEM A BIT AGITATED.

NOT AT ALL, OFFICER! I'M FINE. I AM QUITE DELIGHTED THAT I HAVE ONCE AGAIN ALLAYED YOUR SUSPICIONS! I WISH YOU ALL HEALTH, AND A LITTLE MORE COURTESY. PERHAPS NOW I MIGHT BE ALLOWED TO ENJOY SOME PEACE IN MY HOME. MY VERY WELL-CONSTRUCTED HOME. HA HA.

WHEN THE WALL FELL, THERE SAT NONE OTHER THAN THE
HIDEOUS BEAST WHOSE CRAFT HAD SEDUCED ME INTO
MURDER. I HAD WALLED THE MONSTER UP WITHIN THE TOMB!

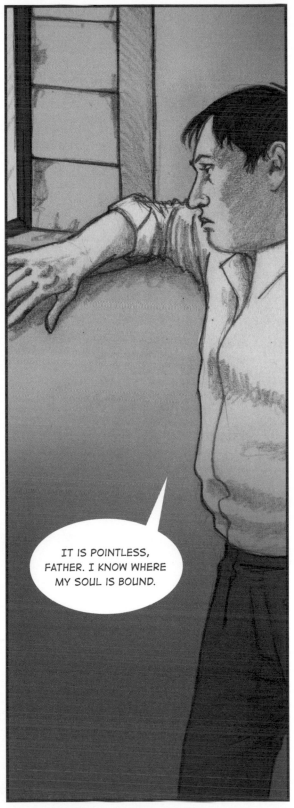

The System of Doctor Tarr
and Professor Fether

I HAVE FOUND OUT THAT THERE IS A PRIVATE MAD HOUSE A FEW MILES FROM HERE. WOULDN'T IT BE DELICIOUS TO VISIT IT? I IMAGINE IT MUST BE FILLED WITH PETRIFYING LUNATICS!

YOU'RE THE LUNATIC! WHY ON EARTH WOULD YOU WANT TO VISIT A PLACE LIKE THAT--AND OGLE AT THOSE UNFORTUNATE PEOPLE?

BESIDES, I VERY MUCH DOUBT IT IS AS FRIGHTENING AS ALL THAT. IF IT IS THE MAISON DE SANTE I'M THINKING OF, IT IS RUN BY AN ACQUAINTANCE OF MY FATHER'S: MONSIEUR MAILLARD, IF I REMEMBER ALRIGHT. A VERY RESPECTABLE, WELL-EDUCATED MAN.

I REMEMBER HIM TELLING MY FATHER ABOUT HIS "SYSTEM OF SOOTHING." THEY AVOID ALL PUNISHMENTS AND NEVER LOCK ANYONE AWAY. THE INMATES ARE LEFT TO WANDER THE HOUSE AND GROUNDS IN THEIR OWN CLOTHES, BUT ARE WATCHED IN SECRET.

AFTER A TWO-HOUR RIDE...

YOU LOOK ALARMED. ARE YOU SURE YOU WANT TO GO IN?

OF COURSE! I'M NO POLTROON!

LOOK, SOMEONE'S THERE.

MONSIEUR MAILLARD, IT IS GOOD TO SEE YOU AGAIN. YOU MAY NOT REMEMBER ME...

I REMEMBER YOU. YOU'RE THE COMTE DE CHAMBORD'S SON. WHAT BRINGS YOU ALL THE WAY OUT HERE?

I AM JUST ON MY WAY TO PERIGUEUX.

BUT MY FRIEND HERE, MONSIEUR DUFOUR, WHO...ER...

...HOPES TO EMBARK ON A CAREER IN THERAPY, VERY MUCH DESIRES A TOUR OF YOUR ESTABLISHMENT.

I KNOW IT IS AN INCONVENIENCE.

NOT AT ALL. I WILL BE MORE THAN HAPPY TO ATTEND TO MONSIEUR DUFOUR.

YOU ARE VERY KIND, MONSIEUR. THAT'S SETTLED THEN. ALRIGHT THEN, CLAUDE. I WILL STAY IN PERIGUEUX TWO DAYS BEFORE MOVING ON. *AU REVOIR*, GENTLEMEN!

140

THE PIANIST! SHE LOOKED VERY FINE IN HER MOURNING ATTIRE BEFORE. WHAT ON EARTH IS SHE WEARING NOW? DOES SHE HAVE NO ONE TO HELP HER??

AN HOUR INTO DINNER...

I MUST ADMIT I MISJUDGED THIS COMPANY. ODD, TO BE SURE, BUT THEY ARE ALL WELL EDUCATED AND RATHER WITTY. I AM SURPRISED THAT THEY TALK SO FREELY ABOUT LUNACY AT DINNER, THOUGH...

MONSIEUR DUFOUR! WE HAD A FELLOW HERE ONCE WHO FANCIED HIMSELF A TEA POT! IS IT NOT STRANGE THAT THIS PARTICULAR QUIRK IS SO COMMON?

THERE IS SCARCELY AN ASYLUM IN FRANCE WHICH CANNOT SUPPLY A HUMAN TEA POT!

AND NOT LONG AGO WE HAD A MAN WHO THOUGHT HE WAS A DONKEY—WHICH ALLEGORICALLY SPEAKING WAS QUITE TRUE. HE WAS A TROUBLESOME PATIENT AND FOR A LONG TIME WOULD EAT NOTHING BUT THISTLES.

BUT OF THIS IDEA WE SOON CURED HIM BY INSISTING HE EAT NOTHING ELSE. THEN HE WAS CONSTANTLY KICKING OUT HIS HEELS...

MR. DE KOCK! I WILL THANK YOU TO BEHAVE YOURSELF! YOU HAVE RUINED MY BROCADE!

UPON MY WORD YOU ARE NEARLY AS GREAT A DONKEY AS THE POOR UNFORTUNATE IMAGINED HIMSELF.

A THOUSAND PARDONS, MADEMOISELLE LAPLACE!

YOU MUST TRY THE VEAL *A LA* ST. MENEHOULT, MONSIEUR.

THANK YOU, NO. TO SAY THE TRUTH, I AM NOT PARTIAL TO VEAL.

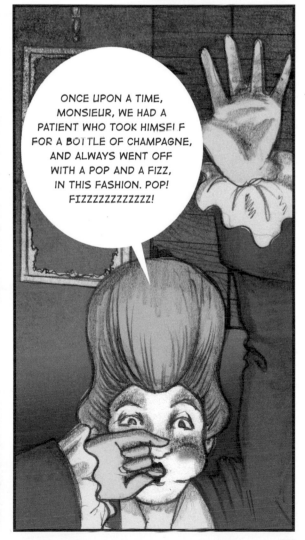

145

HE WAS A GREAT FOOL BEYOND DOUBT, BUT NOT TO BE COMPARED WITH AN INDIVIDUAL WHO BELIEVED HIMSELF TO BE A CORDOVA CHEESE. HE WENT ABOUT WITH A KNIFE IN HIS HAND, SOLICITING HIS FRIENDS TO TRY A SLICE FROM HIS ARM.

AND THEN THERE WAS PETIT GAILLARD, WHO THOUGHT HIMSELF A PINCH OF SNUFF. HE WAS TRULY DISTRESSED BECAUSE HE COULD NOT TAKE HIMSELF BETWEEN HIS OWN FINGER AND THUMB.

149

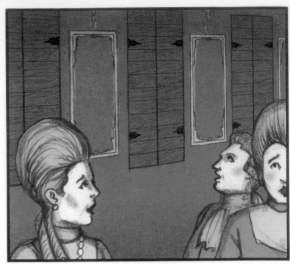

HOLD YOUR TONGUES, EVERY ONE OF YOU!!

SO THESE PEOPLE...THE GENTLEWOMAN WHO GAVE US THE COCK-A-DOODLE-DOO, FOR INSTANCE. SHE IS HARMLESS?

HARMLESS? WHATEVER CAN YOU MEAN?

ONLY SLIGHTLY TOUCHED I MEAN. I TAKE IT SHE IS NOT DANGEROUSLY... AFFECTED?

MON DIEU! WHAT IS IT YOU IMAGINE? MADAME JOYEUSE IS A PARTICULAR OLD FRIEND AND IS AS ABSOLUTELY SANE AS MYSELF.

TO BE SURE, TO BE SURE. AND THEN THE REST OF THESE LADIES AND GENTLEMEN...?

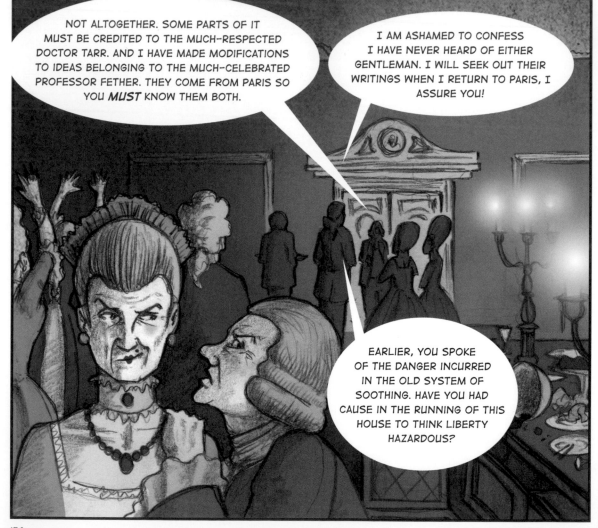

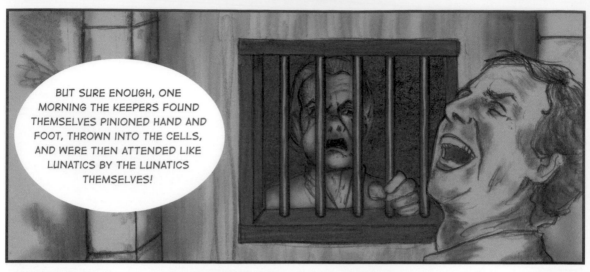

BUT SURE ENOUGH, ONE MORNING THE KEEPERS FOUND THEMSELVES PINIONED HAND AND FOOT, THROWN INTO THE CELLS, AND WERE THEN ATTENDED LIKE LUNATICS BY THE LUNATICS THEMSELVES!

YOU DON'T TELL ME SO! I NEVER HEARD OF ANYTHING SO ABSURD IN MY LIFE!

IT IS THE TRUTH.

AND ALL BECAUSE OF ONE MAN, WHO WAS IN THE PAST A SUPERINTENDENT AT THIS VERY HOUSE. A LUNATIC WHO BELIEVED HE HAD INVENTED A BETTER FORM OF GOVERNMENT.

HE WANTED TO GIVE HIS IDEA A TRIAL AND PERSUADED THE REST OF THE PATIENTS TO JOIN HIM IN HIS COUP.

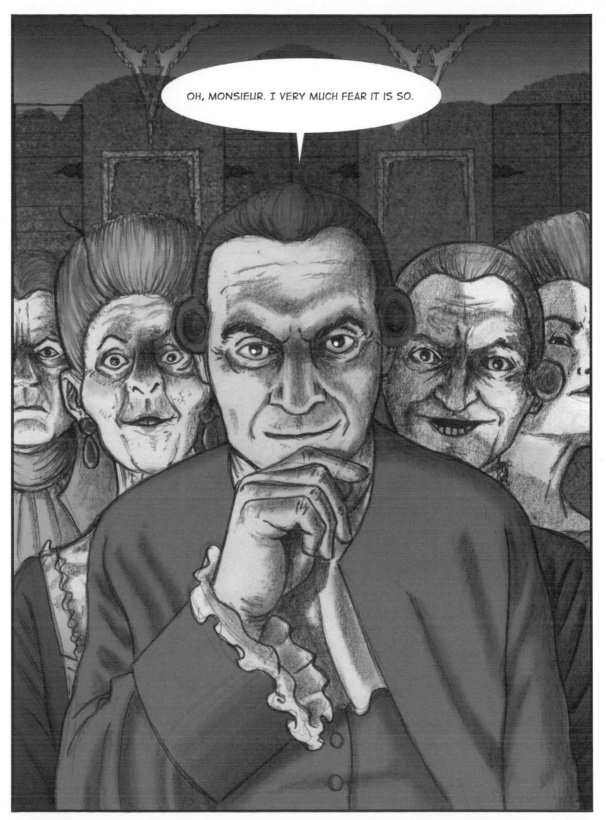

Acknowledgments

Big thanks to my models Jaquie Brown, David Browning, Ben and Barbora Jones, Stephen Pearce, Richard Recardo, and Bob Thompson. Thanks to Quid Publishing, especially Lucy, James, and Harry. Thanks as always to my Ma, brother, and sister for their continued love and support. And to the rest of my family: you're terrific. Thanks to my amazing friends. Special mentions to Richard Recardo, Andrew Casey, Nick Jackson, Sebastian Cheswright Cater, Rebecca Hull, Maxine Doyle, Ben Vincent, Keith Davie, Laura Thomas, Han and Karolien, Bill and Vicky, Jon, Simon, Paul, Jo, Alex and Steph, Adam and Mari, the Bad Apples, the Reckless Records crew, and the Brighton Waterstoners. Love you guys.